HONORED ANCESTORS
A Kentucky Toad History

by
Janice Lee Brannon

The Beehive Press
Lexington, Kentucky
1993

Printed by
6-/5-06
Percetakan NPN & Brothers Sdn. Bhd.
6 & 8, Jalan Berhala,
Off Jalan Tun Sambanthan,
50470 Kuala Lumpur, Malaysia.

Dedicated to
Paula, Scot, Shaun

Please be aware that the author of <u>Honored Ancestors</u> has the deepest regard for nature and all of her creatures. Each of our toad friends was returned to his/her natural habitat, permanently pensioned after one day of stardom.

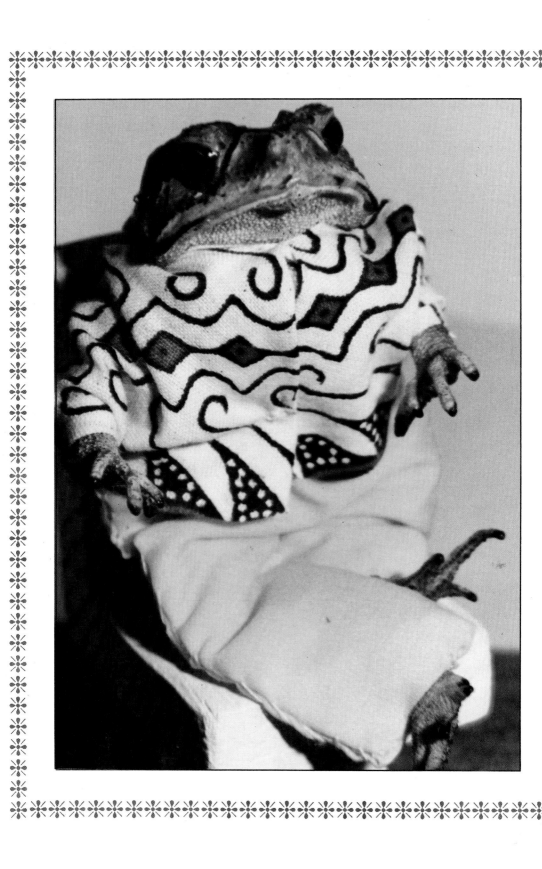

Old Toadus T. Too-Fat,

A toad of some girth,

Lived deep in a hole

In the mouldering earth,

In the quaint country garden

Of old Farmer Flynn,

Whose wife kept the garden

As neat as a pin.

Old Toadus' sweet wife was

A matronly toad,

Who never complained

Of their meager abode.

She easily fixed it

When old Mrs. Flynn

In a frenzy of weeding

Would cave the sides in.

The favorite pastime

Of old Toadus T.

Was telling the tales

Of the Toad Family Tree.

The old toads and young toads

Would gather around,

For all were related

On this plot of ground.

When day reached its end,

The sun's last rays were gone,

The croaking crescendoed

And went on 'til dawn.

"I recollect grandfather

Saying to me,"

'Remember your forefathers,

Young Toadus T.' "

Of character, fortitude,

Pride and great wit,

They faced each new challenge

With courage and grit.

Old Gnat Taniel Gnoone

Was a trailblazing toad,

Who led the way West on

The Wilderness Road.

His father, Tall Feather,

An Indian guide,

Took Miss Hortense Highhop

To be his toad bride.

The haughty Miss Hortense,

A high born toad child,

Fell head over toes

For that toad from the wild.

Our history, however,

Owes most to the quest

Of Tristan, "The Treetoad

Who Opened the West."

His son, Obadiah,

A trapper by trade,

Fell hard for a maiden

With fair skin of jade.

Their children would settle

Kentucky's frontiers,

From Booneville to Bardstown,

True toad pioneers.

They tamed the vast wilderness,

Farmed the new land,

Pressed ever on westward,

The future unplanned.

It's said that Cadwallader

Croaker could sway

Kentucky's great statesman,

The bold Henry Clay.

His eloquence earned him

A place of esteem

As Toadtown's first mayor,

His life's fondest dream.

The audience listened

And croaked their delight

With all of the tales

Toadus told them that night.

A youngster named Tiptoed

Was eager to know,

"Our tree dwelling ancestors,

Where did they go?"

A question that seemed

To be asked without fail,

"Do tree dwelling ancestor

Toads have a tail?"

They heard many stories

Of ancient toad lore,

But still they would shout

"Toadus, tell us some more!"

Well, Lorelei Longleap,

A true southern belle

Once opened an elegant

Frontier hotel.

Her beauty was legend,

But what was soon plain,

Her feminine form held

A first class toad brain.

And Hop-a-long Hank

Hit the lone prairie trails

Where mournful winds blow

And the coyote wails.

Young Fester Flycatcher,

The Marshal's right hand,

Rode clear to Paducah

In search of new land.

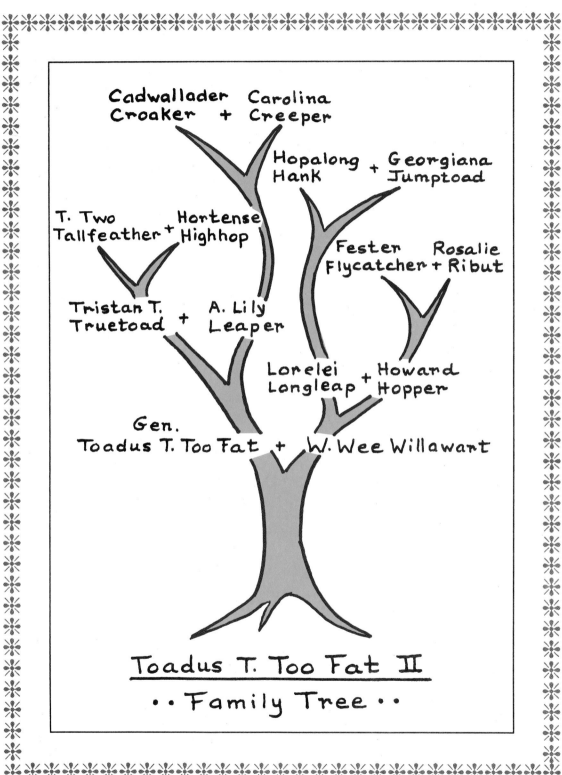

Toadus T. Too Fat II
·· Family Tree ··

So some were outstanding

While others were plain,

But all knew enough

To go out in the rain.

And each had a place

On the toad family tree,

Thus forming the branches

Of toad ancestry.

The rays of the sun

Sought the edge of the sky.

The night shadows gathered

Preparing to fly.

The din of our toad friends

Was dwindling away.

Soon all of the toads

Closed their eyes to the day.

A necklace of dew drops

On spider webs lay,

Suspended like jewels

In the new light of day.

And just as the sun

Finally rose from its bed,

The cobwebs of sleep

Left old Farmer Flynn's head.

The Story of the Story

Paula and Kelly exploded into my sewing room, each holding a small toad dressed in little pants and shirts. They had come begging scraps of material to make some more toad clothes. Having never before in my whole life seen a live toad dressed in clothes, I was beyond amazed and inquired as to precisely how they had managed to put clothes on those wee creatures. Children, with their mainline connection to creativity in operation, know instinctively that the "how" of such matters is inconsequential, so they answered with the obvious "We just did it!" Upon further inquiry I was informed of a developing plan to stage a "Toadus Circus". Paula and her friend Kelly were in charge of wardrobe, while Shaun, Scot, and Kelly's brother Joe were organizing the acts and training the toads. At the moment of speaking, toads were undergoing training for a parachute act. Assuring Paula and Kelly that I would be an eager audience when the circus came to town, I gave them a pile of scraps and they enthusiastically returned to the business of their day.

Some months later I happened to recall that there had been no further mention of the "Toadus Circus". It had in truth been an event I was eager to record, so I was deeply disappointed when they told me the circus had been cancelled because one of the trainees had broken a leg during parachute practice. Obviously, circusing was too dangerous an activity for toads. Although the children had had a grand time planning and preparing for this great event, they seemed to have little concern that the circus did not in fact materialize.

It was in this way in 1971, in a remote area of northeast Thailand, that I was reintroduced to the creative spirit of childhood - that world in which adult concerns are excluded and the "process of play itself" is the goal. And I wanted to play too!

It is rare that adults are allowed, or allow themselves, to participate in that world of pure play, and I thank my three children for having opened the door that encouraged me to do so. I hope that through this book you can join me for a moment.